STOCKING STUMPERS
FOOTBALL EDITION

CHRISTMAS 2006

**By S. Claus
with help from Jeff Kreismer**

Red-Letter Press, Inc.

STOCKING STUMPERS
Copyright ©2006 Red-Letter Press, Inc.
ISBN-10: 0-940462-29-X
ISBN-13: 978-0-940462-29-8
Printed in the United States of America

For information:

Red-Letter Press, Inc.
P.O. Box 393, Saddle River, NJ 07458
www.Red-LetterPress.com

Acknowledgments

A Stocking Stumpers salute to Santa's "subordinate clauses":

Project development coordinator: **Kobus Reyneke**

Cover design and typography: **Christina Chybinski**

Santa illustration: **Jack Kreismer, Sr.**

Editorial: **Jack Kreismer**

A personal message from Santa

'Twas the night before Christmas
and I left the North Pole
to bring to your stocking
a fresh lump of coal;
But St. Nick's got heart
and your sins weren't voluminous,
so I brought you a gift
in lieu of bituminous;
Now since you've escaped
my long list of lumpers,
I've left you instead
Santa's favorite, *Stocking Stumpers*.

Merry Christmas!

S. Claus

STOCKING STUMPERS
FOOTBALL EDITION

CHRISTMAS 2006

THE YEAR IN REVIEW

1. Who was named to replace Paul Tagliabue as Commissioner of the NFL?
2. The Steelers were 21-10 winners over the Seahawks in Super Bowl XL. What is Pittsburgh's overall record in Super Bowl competition?
3. Controversial wide receiver Terrell Owens says he was misquoted in *T.O.*, a book published earlier in the year. What's odd about his claim?
4. On August 12, Cardinals Stadium opened in Glendale, Arizona, where Arizona defeated Pittsburgh, 21-13, in a preseason game. What was Arizona's prior home facility?
5. Rookie running back Reggie Bush wears number 25 for the New Orleans Saints. What number did he wear at USC?

ANSWERS

1. Roger Goodell
2. 5-1
3. It is his autobiography.
4. Sun Devils Stadium
5. 5

EXTRA POINT

"I was going to write myself in, but I was afraid I'd get shot."

-Lincoln Kennedy, Oakland Raiders
tackle, on his decision not to vote

THE NAME GAME

Match the footballer with his real first name.

1. Boomer Esiason   a) Paul
2. Bill Parcells   b) Norman
3. Weeb Ewbank   c) Harold
4. Red Grange   d) Duane
5. Bear Bryant   e) Wilber

ANSWERS

1. B
2. D
3. E
4. C
5. A

EXTRA POINT

"The good news is that our defense is giving up only one touchdown a game. The bad news is that our offense is doing the same."

—Bobby Bowden, on Florida State

PIGSKIN POTPOURRI

1. In the last 50 years, only one team has scored more than 70 points in a game. Name the team.
2. True or false? When the Patriots beat the Rams 20-17 in Super Bowl XXXVI, it marked the first time in the big game's history that the winning points came on the final play of the game.
3. Who was the very first selection of the Houston Texans in the 2002 NFL Expansion Draft?
4. The NFL's largest single game attendance ever was played in what city?
5. What's the yardage penalty if a team attempts a second forward pass behind the line of scrimmage?

ANSWERS

1. The Washington Redskins, in 1966, in a 72-41 win over the New York Giants
2. True- a 48-yard field goal by Adam Vinatieri
3. Five-time Pro Bowl tackle Tony Boselli
4. Mexico City - where 112,376 spectators witnessed an exhibition game at Azteca Stadium in 1994 between the Cowboys and Oilers.
5. Five yards

SECOND GUESSING

1. In 2005, Sean Alexander led the NFL in rushing with 1,880 yards. Who was second?
2. He was the MVP of Super Bowl II.
3. He's currently the second coach in Jacksonville Jaguars history, after Tom Coughlin.
4. A member of the Hall of Fame Class of 2002, his name comes second alphabetically in the Pro Football Hall of Fame.
5. This now defunct football league never made it to its second season and was terminated before 2002.

ANSWERS

1. Tiki Barber, with 1,860 yards.
2. Bart Starr
3. Jack Del Rio
4. George Allen
5. XFL- Extreme Football League

EXTRA POINT

"I'm probably about a 4.9 normally, but when a 280-pound guy is chasing me, I'm a 4.6."

– *John Elway, on the 40-yard dash*

DEAR JOHNS

All of the following are clues to men with the first name "John."

1. A 2003 Super Bowl champion, he's currently a safety with the Denver Broncos.
2. This running back was the MVP of Super Bowl XVII.
3. A Jacksonville defensive tackle, he was the 9th pick in the 2002 NFL draft.
4. This seventh year pro out of South Carolina was traded from the Jets to the Falcons earlier this year.
5. He's a former teammate of the answer to #4, and is now a kicker for the Washington Redskins.

ANSWERS

1. John Lynch
2. John Riggins
3. John Henderson
4. John Abraham
5. John Hall

EXTRA POINT

"The reason women don't play football is because eleven of them would never wear the same outfit in public."
—Phyllis Diller

GIVE ME A VOWEL

Below is a list of five current players' first and last names with vowels omitted. The order of the consonants hasn't been changed. How many can you get?
(Hint: Each player has won a Super Bowl ring.)

1. BRDJHNSN
2. TRYPLML
3. BRTTFVR
4. TMBRDY
5. TRRYHLT

ANSWERS

1. Brad Johnson
2. Troy Polamalu
3. Brett Favre
4. Tom Brady
5. Torry Holt

EXTRA POINT

"Our kicker only had one bad day last year –Saturday."

–*Gary Darnell, Tennessee Tech*
coach, coming off an 0-11 season

NOTICE OPERANDI

How observant are you?

1. What are the colors of the NFL logo?
2. The AFC logo has six of them, and the NFC logo three. What are they?
3. Name the only NFL team that does not have an emblem on its helmet.
4. What color are the pylons on an NFL field?
5. In years gone by, TV viewers often saw a fan in the backdrop sporting a multicolored "do" while holding a banner which referred to what biblical passage?

ANSWERS

1. Red, white and blue
2. Stars
3. The Cleveland Browns
4. Orange
5. John 3:16

BREAKING RECORDS

1. He holds the record for the most consecutive games throwing a touchdown pass.
2. Until present-day punter Jeff Feagles broke his mark, who played the most consecutive games in NFL history?
3. In a single Super Bowl game, who has rushed for more yards than anyone in history?
4. Who has the most touchdowns in Super Bowl history?
5. Including the postseason, which coach has won the most games in NFL history?

ANSWERS

1. Johnny Unitas, 47 games
2. Jim Marshall, 282
3. Timmy Smith, 204 in Super Bowl XXII
4. Jerry Rice, 7 (in 3 games)
5. Don Shula, 347

EXTRA POINT

"You guys pair up in groups of three, then line up in a circle."
–*Bill Peterson*

SUPER NUMERALS

1. Which Super Bowl was the first to be officially called the Super Bowl?
2. What was it called before that?
3. How much was the cheapest ticket to the first Super Bowl?
4. Which Super Bowl was the first to officially use a Roman numeral?
5. What year is Super Bowl L scheduled for?

ANSWERS

1. Super Bowl IV in 1970
2. AFL-NFL World Championship Game
3. $6 and $10 ... $12 seats were also available for wealthier fans.
4. Super Bowl V in 1971
5. 2016 (Let's hope they bag the Roman numeral thing by then.)

THERE'S A DRAFT IN HERE

1. Who was the last running back to be picked number one in the NFL draft? (Hint: The year was 1995.)
2. Who was the Pittsburgh Steelers' very first number one draft choice ever?
   a) Charles Dickens   b) Ernest Hemingway
   c) William Shakespeare d) Stephen King
3. Which NFL team drafted John Elway?
4. What college player was the last overall NFL number-one pick in the 20th century?
5. What year did the NFL and AFL first hold a combined draft?

ANSWERS

1. Ki-Jana Carter of Penn State, by the Cincinnati Bengals
2. C- Shakespeare (a Notre Dame back)
3. The Baltimore Colts
4. Penn State defensive end Courtney Brown,
   by the Cleveland Browns in 2000
5. 1967

EXTRA POINT

"If you see a defensive team with dirt and mud on their backs, they've had a bad day."

-John Madden

HOME SWEET HOME

Name the teams that call these stadiums home.

1. Reliant Stadium
2. Lincoln Financial Field
3. Gillette Stadium
4. Ralph Wilson Stadium
5. Qualcomm Stadium

ANSWERS

1. Houston Texans
2. Philadelphia Eagles
3. New England Patriots
4. Buffalo Bills
5. San Diego Chargers

EXTRA POINT

"The trouble with referees is that they know the rules,
but they do not know the game."
-*Bill Shankly*

SECOND GUESSING II

1. David Carr of Fresno State was selected by the expansion Houston Texans as the number one pick in the 2002 NFL draft. Who was second?
2. Who was the second defensive back ever to win the Super Bowl MVP? (Hint: It was Super Bowl XXX)
3. He comes second alphabetically in the NFL Hall of Fame. Can you name him?
4. Tom Dempsey kicked an NFL record 63-yard field goal in 1970. Who was the second to do it?
5. This Viking was second in the league in rushing with 1,521 yards in 2000 before retiring the next year. Name him.

ANSWERS

1. Julius Peppers
2. Larry Brown
3. George Allen
4. Jason Elam
5. Robert Smith

QUOTE, UNQUOTE

When former defensive lineman Alex Karras was asked to name the most profitable type of writing, he responded, "Ransom ... " Finish the quote by answering the following clues and writing the boxed letter in the corresponding space at the bottom of the page.

1. They have yet to play in a Super Bowl. __ __ __ (__) __
2. Woody Hayes coached there. __ __ __ (__) __ __ __ __ __
3. Last name of the first woman to own an NFL team

   __ __ __ __ (__) __ __ __ __
4. Only player to record two safeties in an NFL game

   __ __ __ __ __ __ __ (__) __
5. Only NFL team to be owned by a city __ __ __ __ __ __ (__)

$$\overline{} \ \ \overline{} \ \ \overline{} \ \ \overline{} \ \ \overline{}$$
1   2   3   4   5

ANSWERS

1. L I O (N) S
2. O H I (O) S T A T E
3. F R O N (T) I E R E
4. F R E D D R Y (E) R
5. P A C K E R (S)
   N O T E S

MULTI-SPORT

1. What Cleveland Browns Hall of Fame quarterback also played pro basketball?
2. Who hit a home run (in 1989) for the Yankees less than a week before his NFL debut?
3. Who played briefly for the Yankees in 1919 before moving on to become a player/coach/owner/legend in the NFL?
4. Name the man who was an Olympic bobsledder and a footballer who played for the Vikings, Cowboys and Giants to name a few.
5. Do you know the defensive lineman from Michigan State who was the first pick of the 1967 NFL draft and was also an 11th round pick of the NBA Bullets that year?

ANSWERS

1. Otto Graham
2. Deion Sanders
3. George Halas
4. Herschel Walker
5. Bubba Smith

LAUGH-IN TIME-OUT

See if you can answer some of Santa's favorite football groaners provided by resident North Pole jokester Henny Elfman.

1. How many quarterbacks does it take to screw in a light bulb?
2. What do you call an out-of-control Baltimore offensive lineman?
3. What do you call a New Orleans Saint wearing a Super Bowl ring?
4. What do you call a football player with good intuition?
5. What's a coach's least favorite dessert?

ANSWERS

1. None ... They pass the job to a receiver.
2. A Raven lunatic
3. Thief
4. A hunchback
5. Turnovers

EXTRA POINT

"Football is, after all, a wonderful way to get rid of aggression without having to go to jail for it."

-Heywood Hale Broun

THE NUMBERS GAME

See if you can score on these retired numbers
or if you should just hang 'em up yourself.

1. Five NFL teams have retired the number 12. Four of them were for quarterbacks. How many of the five do you know?
2. The Browns retired the uniform number of Ernie Davis, a Heisman Trophy winner who never played a down for them as he died of leukemia. What was that number?
3. What NFL team has retired the most uniform numbers?
4. How come the Dallas Cowboys haven't retired any uniform numbers?
5. Two players with the last name "Brown" have had their numbers retired. Name the players, the team and the numbers.

ANSWERS

1. The number 12 was retired by the Bills for Jim Kelly, by the Dolphins for Bob Griese, by the Jets for Joe Namath and by the 49ers for John Brodie. The Seahawks retired number 12 for "the fans/ the twelfth man."
2. 45
3. The Chicago Bears, 13
4. They have a Ring of Honor around Texas Stadium which depicts the name and number of the players they so choose to recognize.
5. Jim Brown, #32 by the Cleveland Browns and Jerome Brown, #99 by the Philadelphia Eagles

PASSING FANCIES

1. Fran Tarkenton's 342nd and last touchdown pass was caught by what current sportscaster?
2. Who has thrown a record seven Super Bowl interceptions?
3. Who's the odd man out: Y.A. Tittle, Dan Fouts, Steve Grogan or Johnny Unitas? (Hint: Think "numbers.")
4. What New York Yankees minor league player hit .318 in 1982 and later became a Super Bowl-winning quarterback?
5. He wore number 3 while quarterbacking for the Fighting Irish and wore the number 16 in the pros. Name him.

ANSWERS

1. Ahmad Rashad
2. Jim Kelly
3. Johnny Unitas ... While all have had their numbers retired, Unitas wore the number 19; all the others wore the number 14.
4. John Elway
5. Joe Montana

PIGSKIN POTPOURRI

1. What NFL team originally drafted Brett Favre?
2. The Pete Rozelle Award is given to whom?
3. What NFL head coach coined the term "nickel defense?" (Hint: He led the 1972 Washington Redskins to the Super Bowl.)
4. When the Bears defeated the Giants, 14-10, for the NFL title in 1963, where was the game played?
   a) Comiskey Park b) Soldier Field c) Wrigley Field d) Sally Field
5. True or false? If a quarterback throws a pass and it accidentally hits an official, the down is replayed.

ANSWERS

1. Atlanta Falcons
2. The Super Bowl MVP
3. George Allen
4. C
5. False – An official is considered part of the playing field.

EXTRA POINT

"Jerry Rice has more touchdowns than NASA."

-Roy Firestone

SCREEN TEST

Match the actor or actors that starred in these football flicks.

1. *Remember the Titans*
2. *Rudy*
3. *Jerry Maguire*
4. *The Replacements*
5. *Any Given Sunday*

a) Tom Cruise
b) Denzel Washington
c) Sean Astin
d) Al Pacino and Jamie Foxx
e) Keanu Reeves and Gene Hackman

ANSWERS

1. B
2. C
3. A
4. E
5. D

EXTRA POINT

"Most football teams are temperamental.
That's 90% temper and 10% mental."
-*Doug Plank*

PHRASE CRAZE

Santa loves brain teasers. Help him figure out
what pigskin phrases these items represent.

1. F
   I
   R
   S
   T

2. END
   END

3. RETRAUQ

4. PAS_

5. REVERSE
   REVERSE

ANSWERS

1. First down
2. End over end
3. Quarterback
4. Incomplete pass
5. Double reverse

COLLEGE CORNUCOPIA

1. Only three players led the NCAA in rushing and then led the NFL in rushing the following year. Can you name any of them?
2. Halfback Jay Berwanger was the NFL's first number one draft choice ever (by the Eagles in 1936). What other distinctive "first" did he earn while playing for the University of Chicago?
3. Who led college football in rushing in 1971 and later went on to become a *Hill Street Blues* star?
4. Which stadium has the largest capacity of any football venue in the country?
5. In 2004, he broke the NCAA Division 1-A single game rushing record with 406 yards. Name him.

ANSWERS

1. George Rogers, in 1981; Earl Campbell, 1978; and Byron White, 1938
2. He was the first Heisman Trophy winner.
3. Ed Marinaro
4. Michigan Stadium in Ann Arbor
5. LaDainian Tomlinson, for TCU in a victory over UTEP.

KEEPING UP WITH THE JONESES

As the above suggests, the last name is Jones.
What's the first name?

1. He was the only Jones to rush for over 1,000 yards in 2005.
2. This linebacker out of Florida State was the Jets top pick in 1993.
3. Inducted into the Hall of Fame in 1991, this eleven year Chicago Bear appeared in seven consecutive Pro Bowls.
4. He was one of the Rams "Fearsome Foursome".
5. On December 15, 1974, this Colts quarterback set a record by completing 17 passes in a row against the Jets.

ANSWERS

1. Thomas Jones
2. Marvin Jones
3. Stan Jones
4. Deacon Jones
5. Bert Jones

EXTRA POINT

"It is committee meetings, called huddles, separated by outbursts of violence."

-George Will, on football

NOT YOUR AVERAGE JOE

Santa will consider you Joe College if you can come up with the answers to the questions below, all of whom are people named Joe.

1. He's the only player to win three Super Bowl MVP awards.
2. He has a Super Bowl ring and two Pro Bowl MVP awards.
3. This quarterback was voted the NFL's regular season MVP in 1983.
4. He's infamous for fumbling an unnecessary handoff at the end of the game and blowing the Giants sure victory over the Eagles.
5. Playing in the '50s and '60s, he was the first player in NFL history to gain 1,000 yards in two consecutive seasons.

ANSWERS

1. Joe Montana
2. Joe Namath
3. Joe Theismann
4. Joe Pisarcik
5. Joe Perry

HEADLINE-DATELINE

Match the event with the year it occurred.

1. JIM BROWN SCORES 43	a)	1984
2. FLUTIE'S MIRACLE TAMES HURRICANES	b)	1967
3. GREEN BAY WINS FIRST SUPER BOWL	c)	1969
4. GRIFFIN WINS SECOND HEISMAN	d)	1956
5. NAMATH GUARANTEES VICTORY, JETS WIN	e)	1975

ANSWERS

1. D
2. A
3. B
4. E
5. C

EXTRA POINT

"The minute you think you've got it made, disaster is just around the corner."

-Penn State coach Joe Paterno

PIGSKIN POTPOURRI

1. Which NFL team has hosted a Thanksgiving Day game every year since the Great Depression?
2. Who was the "Alabama Antelope?"
3. What was the nickname of the gang that blocked for the Four Horsemen of Notre Dame?
4. Which two college football teams vie for the Little Brown Jug?
5. I caught 12 passes in the 1958 NFL Championship and later coached the New England Patriots in the Super Bowl. Who am I?

ANSWERS

1. The Detroit Lions
2. Don Hutson
3. The Seven Mules
4. Michigan and Minnesota
5. Raymond Berry, who played with the Colts in '58 and took New England to Super Bowl XX

PRIZE PACKAGES

1. In 1916, Georgia Tech clobbered Cumberland College, 222-0 in college football's most lopsided score in history. Who was Georgia Tech's coach? (Hint: Remember the category.)
2. Who gets the Outland Trophy? (Hint: Steve Emtman, Jonathan Ogden and Orlando Pace have all won it.)
3. What trophy is given to the Super Bowl MVP?
4. Designed by Tiffany and Company, it was originally called the World Championship Game Trophy. Name it.
5. Who receives the Grey Cup?

ANSWERS

1. John Heisman – for whom the trophy was named
2. College's top interior lineman
3. The Pete Rozelle Trophy
4. The Vince Lombardi Trophy
5. The Canadian Football League champion

EXTRA POINT

"Football is not a contact sport, it's a collision sport.
Dancing is a good example of a contact sport."

-Duffy Daugherty

A SIMPLE YES OR NO WILL DO

1. Are there any NFL teams with nicknames that do not end in "s?"
2. Did the Lions and Cowboys ever play each other on Thanksgiving?
3. Is Jim Thorpe in the Pro Football Hall of Fame?
4. Has every team in the AFC West been to a Super Bowl?
5. Were the Steagles once an NFL team?

ANSWERS

1. No
2. No
3. Yes – He was a charter member in 1963.
4. Yes
5. Yes – In 1943, because of the wartime manpower shortage, the Steelers and Eagles merged to become the Steagles.

NAME THAT TEAM

Try to decipher each team based on the clues provided.

1. Fans selected their city's team name in honor of one of the works of American poet Edgar Allan Poe.
2. Team owner Jerry Richardson's son Mark was responsible for selecting this franchise's name.
3. Shortly after they began play as the "Steers", they changed their name to the "Rangers." At the same time, however, a baseball team began play in the same state under that name, and to avoid confusion, the city changed its team's name to this.
4. Owner Tim Mara "borrowed" his team name from the city's Major League Baseball team, something that wasn't uncommon at the time.
5. This NFC team name was selected to recognize the men of the gold rush in the Sierra Nevada Mountains.

ANSWERS

1. **Baltimore** Ravens – The city named its team in honor of **Poe's** poem *The Raven*.
2. **Carolina** Panthers
3. **Dallas** Cowboys, named by Clint Murchison Jr. and **Bedford** Wynne, the two owners of the new NFL team
4. **New York** Giants – The name was taken from baseball's **Giants** in the 1920's.
5. **San Francisco** 49ers

DEE-FENSE!

1. Who was the number one overall pick in the 2006 NFL Draft?
2. Who has recorded the most sacks in NFL History?
3. Who holds the Super Bowl record for the most sacks in a single game?
4. What were former Jets Mark Gastineau, Joe Klecko, Abdul Salaam, and Marty Lyons better known as?
5. True or false? No cornerback has ever won the Super Bowl MVP.

ANSWERS

1. Mario Williams, defensive end, NC State, by the Houston Texans.
2. Bruce Smith, 200
3. Reggie White-3 in Super Bowl XXXI
4. The New York Sack Exchange
5. False-Larry Brown of Dallas won it in Super Bowl XXX.

EXTRA POINT

"Most of my clichés aren't original."
–Chuck Knox

CONFERENCE CALL

Match the college team with its Division 1 conference.

1. Virginia Tech
2. Marshall
3. Nebraska
4. San Jose State
5. Air Force

a. Big 12
b. Western Athletic Conference
c. Conference U.S.A.
d. Mountain West
e. ACC

ANSWERS

1. e
2. c
3. a
4. b
5. d

SCRAMBLE

Santa's new computer has gone garbledegook!
Help him unscramble the last names of the football players below.
(Hint: All have been Heisman Trophy winners.)

1. DOSWONO
2. TEULFI
3. KWEENI
4. LIAWSMLI
5. MARPEL

ANSWERS

1. Charles WOODSON
2. Doug FLUTIE
3. Chris WEINKE
4. Ricky WILLIAMS
5. Carson PALMER

EXTRA POINT

"Pro football is a mean game, ideally played by mean men. If it builds character, so does street mugging."

- Larry King, TV host

PIGSKIN POTPOURRI

1. Who's the only player to have earned Super Bowl rings with three different teams?
2. Who holds the record for the highest punting average in a single season?
3. With what team did Steve Young start his career?
4. How many NFL teams have bird nicknames?
5. What NFL team originally drafted Joe Namath?

ANSWERS

1. Matt Millen – He won rings with the Raiders, 49ers, and Redskins.
2. Sammy Baugh
3. Tampa Bay Buccaneers
4. 5 – Cardinals, Falcons, Ravens, Eagles, Seahawks
5. St. Louis Cardinals

THE HALL OF NAMES

Do you know the first names of these NFL Hall of Famers?

1. Crazy Legs Hirsch
2. Weeb Ewbank
3. Joe Greene
4. Deacon Jones
5. Bart Starr

ANSWERS

1. Elroy
2. Wilber
3. Charles
4. Eugene
5. David

PRIZE PACKAGES

Match the following college achievements
with the award that the winner receives.

1. Top Division 1-AA player
2. Top team (voted by writers)
3. Top interior lineman
4. Best defensive back
5. Best quarterback

a) Outland Trophy
b) Payton Award
c) Thorpe Award
d) Grantland Rice Trophy
e) O'Brien Award

ANSWERS

1. B
2. D
3. A
4. C
5. E

EXTRA POINT

"We have a strange and wonderful relationship.
He's strange and I'm wonderful."

–Mike Ditka, on his relationship
with Jim McMahon

TAKE ME OUT TO THE OLD BALLPARK

Name the NFL team that used to play in these stadiums.

1. Wrigley Field
2. Municipal Stadium
3. Orange Bowl
4. Houlihan Stadium
5. RFK Stadium

ANSWERS

1. Chicago Bears
2. Cleveland Browns
3. Miami Dolphins
4. Tampa Bay Buccaneers
5. Washington Redskins

EXTRA POINT

"Anyone can have an off decade."

- Larry Cole, Dallas Cowboys,
after going 11 years between
scoring touchdowns

BY THE NUMBERS

1. How many footballs does the home team provide for a game?
2. How much time is put on the play clock between downs?
3. How wide is a football field?
4. On what yard line does the kickoff take place?
5. Unsportsmanlike conduct will earn a team a penalty of how many yards?

ANSWERS

1. 24
2. 40 seconds
3. 53 1/3 yards or 160 feet
4. The kicking team's 30 yard line
5. 15

EXTRA POINT

"We definitely will be improved this year. Last year
we lost 10 games. This year we only scheduled nine."

-Ray Jenkins, former Montana State coach

FRANKLY, MY DEAR

The following questions
all have names or places with "Frank" in them.

1. Where did the Philadelphia Eagles play their home games
   before Veterans Stadium was built?
2. He played a part in the Music City Miracle in 2000.
3. Who was the NFL MVP in 1956?
4. They're one of the six teams in NFL Europe.
5. What Patriots kicker led the NFL in scoring in 1986?

ANSWERS

1. Franklin Field
2. Frank Wycheck
3. Frank Gifford
4. Frankfurt Galaxy
5. Tony Franklin

A SIMPLE YES OR NO WILL DO

1. Has any team ever won three Super Bowls in a row?
2. Has any defensive player won the Heisman Trophy in the last 50 years?
3. Did Walter Payton miss a game in his entire 13-year career?
4. Has there ever been a safety in the Super Bowl?
5. Are there any kickers or punters currently in the NFL Hall of Fame?

ANSWERS

1. No
2. Yes – Only once. Charles Woodson, CB from Michigan, won the award in 1997.
3. Yes – He missed one.
4. Yes – Five safeties have been recorded, each in a different game.
5. Yes – One ... placekicker Jan Stenerud, who played from 1967 to 1985

HEADLINE – DATELINE

Match the event with the year it occurred.

1. DENVER WINS THEIR FIRST SUPER BOWL   a. 2001
2. SHULA BECOMES WINNINGEST COACH   b. 1988
3. JAGUARS, PANTHERS PLAY FIRST GAMES   c. 1993
4. STRAHAN SETS SACK RECORD   d. 1998
5. DITKA, BILETNIKOFF INDUCTED TO HALL   e. 1995

ANSWERS

1. d
2. c
3. e
4. a
5. b

EXTRA POINT

"I'm expecting a good season. I don't know why.
Just ignorance, I guess."

*- Abe Martin, TCU football coach,
on the kind of season he expects*

PIGSKIN POTPOURRI

1. Four quarterbacks were named to the NFL's 75th Anniversary All-Time Team ten years ago. How many can you name?
2. By what name were the Bears formerly known as?
3. Who was the first congressman to be inducted into the Pro Football Hall of Fame?
4. In the 1995 NFL Draft, the Panthers and Jaguars participated for the first time. Which expansion team had the higher pick?
5. How many teams did Warren Moon play for during his NFL career?

ANSWERS

1. Joe Montana, Johnny Unitas, Sammy Baugh, and Otto Graham
2. Decatur Staleys
3. Steve Largent, a former Seattle Seahawks wide receiver,was the Republican U.S. Representative from Oklahoma in 1995.
4. The Jaguars – Jacksonville selected Tony Boselli with the second pick. Carolina took Kerry Collins at #5.
5. 4 – Oilers, Vikings, Seahawks, Chiefs (Moon also played for the Edmonton Eskimos in the CFL before joining the NFL.)

ON THE MOVE

Match the team with the former city in which it played.

1. Tennessee Titans
2. Washington Redskins
3. Kansas City Chiefs
4. Oakland Raiders
5. Indianapolis Colts

a. Baltimore
b. Dallas
c. Boston
d. Houston
e. Los Angeles

ANSWERS

1. d
2. c
3. b
4. e
5. a

EXTRA POINT

"I think it would be a good idea."

- John McKay, Tampa Bay Buccaneers
coach, when asked about his team's
execution after a loss

LAST CALL

With which team did each of these players end their careers?

1. Eric Dickerson
2. Mike Ditka
3. Joe Namath
4. Tony Dorsett
5. Don Maynard

ANSWERS

1. Atlanta Falcons
2. Dallas Cowboys
3. L.A. Rams
4. Denver Broncos
5. St. Louis Cardinals

EXTRA POINT

"Probably the Beatles' white album."

- Steve Largent, former Seattle Seahawk,
on which record he will cherish the most

ODDS AND ENDS

The term "odds" and/or "ends" is involved
in the questions and/or answers in this quiz.

1. In 2000, the Hall of Fame selection committee chose what
   tight end as a member of the all-time NFL team?
2. Who's the odd man out here: Tom Brady, Daunte Culpepper,
   Brett Favre, Matt Hasselbeck? (Hint: Think "Draft")
3. If a blocked punt goes out of the kicking team's end zone,
   is it ruled a safety?
4. In 1995, he ended his career having played more seasons with
   one team than any other player in NFL history. Who is he?
5. What was odd about the Panthers 1-15 record for the
   2001 season?

ANSWERS

1. John Mackey
2. Tom Brady-He's the only one of the four that's currently on the team that drafted him.
3. Yes
4. Jackie Slater –He played all 20 years of his career with the Rams.
5. They won their first game in week one of the season and set an NFL record of losing 15 straight games after their victory.

AUTHOR! AUTHOR!

1. In his book, *Just Give Me The Damn Ball!*, this wide receiver described life during his rookie season in the NFL during which his team went 1-15.

2. This quarterback wrote *All Things Possible*, after his unbelievable season in 1999.

3. Can you name the former Dallas Cowboy wide receiver who wrote the bestselling novel *North Dallas Forty*?

4. He wrote, *The Final Season: My Last Year As Head Coach In The NFL* in 2000, but later decided to take another coaching job in 2003.

5. In 2001, this four-time Super Bowl winner released his book, *It's Only A Game*.

ANSWERS

1. Keyshawn Johnson
2. Kurt Warner
3. Pete Gent
4. Bill Parcells
5. Terry Bradshaw

EXTRA POINT

"He said, 'Gosh, Dad, that mean's we're not going to any more bowl games.'"

-Jim Colletto, Purdue football coach and former assistant at Arizona State and Ohio State, on his 11-year-old son's reaction after he took the job with the Boilermakers

'TIS THE SEASON

1. This Hall of Fame running back and Super Bowl MVP was born on Christmas Day, 1946.

2. On Christmas Eve in 1974, this quarterback became the first Super Bowl MVP to be named a head coach. Who is he?

3. 'Twas the day after Christmas in 1955 when this quarterback bid farewell to football in grand style by scoring two touchdowns and throwing for two more as the Browns beat the Rams, 38-14, for the NFL championship. Name him.

4. The Packers won their third straight NFL title by defeating the Cowboys 21-17, at Lambeau Field in Green Bay on New Year's Eve in 1967. This contest, played in frigid conditions, has been given what nickname?

5. Finally, what did the Notre Dame football coach write in his holiday cards?

ANSWERS

1. Larry Csonka
2. Bart Starr, MVP of Super Bowls I and II, became coach of the Green Bay Packers.
3. Otto Graham
4. The Ice Bowl
5. "Irish You a Merry Christmas" …And so does Santa!